The Garden Stories

KATE GRIFFIN

Illustrated by

Marleen Starksfield-Lowe

13 December 1979 — 7 November 2020

ISBN: 978-1-78324-212-2

Published by Wordzworth
www.wordzworth.com

Dedicated

to

Polly Starksfield-Lowe

Marleen and 'The Garden Stories'

Many years ago I was asked to put together three addresses or meditations for a quiet garden day at a monastery. I told them that I couldn't do that but I could write three stories. And so I did. I have no idea what the participants thought of it but I do know that the monk who was organising it liked them and we toyed with the idea of publishing them then but it didn't happen.

A few years later I had cause to fish them out. I realised that they would benefit from illustrations and I thought of Marleen. I had seen enough of her work to realise that if she liked them then she was the person for it. I was very tentative because it was a big ask. I need not have worried. As soon as I saw the first one, I knew it was perfect: it was more than perfect; it wasn't just an illustration, it was so much part of the creation that it was a collaboration: she had got into the imaginative process in a way that it was as if she had been there at the outset. I cannot now think of the stories without Marleen's pictures. Sky's knobbly knees make me weep.

We intended to publish them and initially Marleen was going to do the book designing and preparation for publication.

We were just about to get together to exchange ideas and get on with the practicalities when lockdown happened and we were pinned in our houses. I think we both thought that we had time on our side.

Very sadly we didn't. Marleen was diagnosed with acute myeloid leukaemia in the summer of 2019 and died on 7 November 2020.

This book is a tribute to a wonderful, vibrant, talented, artist; a devoted and caring friend and family member.

This is from Sandi, Marleen's mother and Stephen, her brother:

"Although Marleen is no longer with us her love and artistry
will live on Polly, the baby girl she lived and fought for."

This is from Helen Starkswood, Marleen's sister-in-law:

"A few Christmases ago my wonderful wordsmith of an aunt showed us
a picture Marleen had drawn for her story. It was a beautiful picture of a
girl with knobbly knees that Kate said was perfect. We loved it and were
so excited to see what Marleen was going to produce next. Over the next
few months I saw a few more pictures but then other events took over...

Marleen continued to instil a love of arts into Polly. They were always
sending me photos of their latest projects and Polly was always so excited
about her handiwork. The last photo Marleen sent was of Polly with her
face painted for Halloween, "It was a rushed job but I decided if you can't
have Halloween, you can still be a snow leopard!" In those last few months,
we had countless random conversations about anything and everything
and, while we decided we'd never agree over the sexiest Star Trek captain
or whether mint tea and rum was a hot mojito or not, we would always
agree that Polly is, and always will be, amazing. Marleen may have been
taken from us but she will live on through these illustrations and Polly."

Polly is now seven, very bright, loving and responsive and really has inherited her mother's skills.

The book is dedicated to Polly and this is a self-portrait she did.

Kate Griffin
July 2021

The
Beach
Garden

From a distance the figure was small and crouched, even for a moment you could think it was a rock, only there weren't any rocks on this coast. No rocks, only sand and the occasional reach of shingle. But no rocks.

Then if you looked at it for a while there were movements so then if not a rock, possibly an animal. A sick animal. A seal perhaps, or a dog.

The possibility of a human came last.

A long way last.

That was three days ago. Three days that she had come back to see if the figure was still there and each time it was. Not always at exactly the same time, but always in the same place.

And it had about it, its actions, a private feel of something almost furtive, engrossed certainly. A task. Work that precluded anyone else. Intrusion, it felt like to go closer.

And so the child went very slowly. Silently on the sand in her bare feet. Until she could see what the undertaking was. The little garden, a delight of paths and mounds, and walls and hedges, pavements and patios. Built from twigs and stones, pebbles and feathers. Orange twine and grey string and bits of rope and shells.

It was done with care, that much was obvious; each stone, bleached twig, greasy feather, placed with an exhausting precision. Exhausting because it was all to be done again. Every day. A strange, hard, dry discipline that had no meaning.

Sky – for that was the child's name – hunkered down and watched.

Until she could not bear the anxiety of it, the terror of its loss and the thought of the roiling waves uncomprehendingly consuming the little paradise and almost cried out the words.

"It'll get taken."

And the old woman, for that was what it was, turned a bony head towards her, and eyes as greeny blue and faded as the horizon gazed at the child.

And the child blundered on, "You should have done it up under the dunes. If you want it to be safe."

"And why should I want it to be safe?" A voice creaky with disuse, with an ancient edge of a distant country.

And the child was baffled, her life was ringed around with safety. Hands held to cross a road, hedges and walls and metal fences to stop unimaginable nasty things happening to her, to stop her doing unimaginably nasty things. She couldn't picture a world in which such fears were not to be considered.

"The tide, you see," she said, in case the old woman had missed out on learning these things. "The tide'll take it."

"And what would I do tomorrow?"

There was nothing to say to that.

She could not imagine her mother saying anything like that. Her mother's tomorrows were full, would always be full. With plans and plots and tactics and strategies, and keeping one step ahead and ships coming home and lottery tickets winning, "You'll see," her mother had said. "It'll all work out. It'll be all right when..." And the 'when' went on and on for ever, and had no shape or ending beyond the moment the tongue met the teeth, leaving an endless gentle possibility. Like the sea.

She looked out to the horizon. The sea was quieter but still it rolled and surged.

Now, after three days, it had become a background to her new life down here on the coast. A new start, a complete break. Her mother's words. Again.

The figure beside her went on, busying itself, because Sky could not rid herself of the idea that this person was an it, not a her. Busy, delicate movements, twig-thin fingers, knobbly, with skin as pulled and tight and wrinkled as skin on boiled milk, blue veins and filthy nails, picking and selecting and rejecting and choosing. According to some unfathomable map or chart that was in her head.

"Is it the same every day, then?"

The old head reared up, and stared at Sky.

"How can it be?"

And of course, as Sky thought about it, it couldn't be. Washed clean and flattened by the waves each day there was no way it could be reproduced. The twigs would float away, fetch up along the shore, stones would roll and move, the string and twine would unravel, the shells would be fleshed by the sand, the feathers would fly. Only they wouldn't of course. Well, only a little in the wind.

"How can you tell how it's going to be, then?"

The old eyes found Sky's and held them for a long moment.

Then she laughed. A harsh, clatter from deep in her throat, unused and creaky as a sea-rusted door hinge.

"What's your name?" the old woman asked instead of answering the question.

Sky hesitated, she was used to this. For a moment she was tempted to tell a lie, opt for Jessica, or Emma. There were three of each in her class. But she might be found out.

"Sky," she muttered.

"Speak up."

"Sky."

"What kind of name is that?"

"It's a hippy name."

"Bet they tease you at school."

"Yup."

"Change it. Become someone different. I do it all the time. It's something that gets easier with practice. After a while you don't notice who you are.

Which one you are. It's like the foundling child in a fairy tale. Is she really a peasant or a princess?"

"You're funny, you."

"And you're rude."

"I was only saying."

"Only saying can be rude."

But Sky stayed where she was, and then very tentatively she reached across and placed a stone in a corner of the garden. It was rough and dark red. And she stood it on its end like it was a tower. The old woman looked at her, and then at the tower.

Then she laughed again.

"That was a brick. From the old village."

"What village?"

"It's under the sea."

Sky knew that was stupid, as stupid as building a garden where the tide would destroy it every day, but she didn't say anything.

The old woman sent her away to find the smallest shell on the beach and that was stupid too, because you would never know if it was the smallest shell, and she knew that she'd been sent away just to be sent away, like her mother sometimes used to say to dig a hole to Australia just to get rid of her for a while.

She went and sat on a breakwater and watched the sea. The little waves at the edge looked like ginger beer, only she knew that was a cheat because when you tasted them they were just salty and gritty and not at all gingery.

It all felt like a cheat. The smallest shell, the waves that weren't what they looked like, villages under the sea and a garden that wouldn't last. And the cheating bit sat in her tummy and made her feel sick. Like nothing was solid and real and going to last more than anything else. Like Dad going

away and mum not talking about him and pretending to some people that he'd died and having too many new starts and complete breaks.

She'd been to three schools and at each one she'd had to go through the "What kind of name is that?" bit. Mrs Patterson had got cross when she said that she'd rather be called Mud. Well, not cross but kind of trying to be sympathetic and exasperated at the same time about parents that would call a child Sky. Like the way she expected Sky to be good at art and poetry and all she really wanted to do was to stay in at break time and get on with the next bit in the maths book only you couldn't say stuff like that because everyone thought you were really weird, weirder than having a name like Sky. So you had to do the cheating bit. Like the old woman said about being someone else all the time. Peasant or princess. In stories it was easy because the princesses all pretended to be peasants anyway, until it all came right at the end.

After what seemed like hours the old woman made her way back up the sand and into the dunes, along one of those tracks that weren't really there because the sand had blown all over them. And Sky followed. Trying to pretend that she wasn't. Exploring. Robinson Crusoe. Landed on the beach and looking for food. It wasn't difficult because the dry sand up under the concrete sea wall was deep and heavy going and made her legs feel stuck. She could easily do the exhausted-and-dopey-with-hunger thing.

Up in the dunes she thought she could follow the old woman's footsteps, but there were just the dented bits which could be anything or anyone at any time. It was scary because she couldn't see where she was. She could hear the sea over on her left so she knew that over on her right was the land, but all around her was only the dunes, with hundreds of paths which just petered out after a few yards. Scary but exciting. She went away from the sea until she could see the farm land below her. Flat and patchworky, like the chess board in 'Alice through the looking glass'. And down below, kind of tucked into the ugly scrubby cowering trees was a caravan. Hidden almost, because it was all mossy and green. And a washing line with a towel on it. She could just hear the door on the caravan click shut. She tried to make her way down and it was strange how quickly the sound of the sea died away and the wind dropped.

There were brambles on the warm side of the dunes and the bushes were dark and smelly. It was where people went to pee, because there were no public toilets. It wasn't the kind of seaside that had public toilets. Or ice-creams and postcards.

She had to climb over a barbed wire fence but it was obviously what everyone else did as it was all bent down. Then she was on a rough track which led to the caravan.

The interior of the caravan was dark and musty. It felt like a real adventure when the old woman had opened the door and called to her. She was sure that she hadn't been seen when she had crouched down in the bushes, but it was all part of what she was expecting the day to do. Anyway, it wasn't like going off with a man like Amy had done after school and had been nearly captured, only Sky was never sure that it was true as Amy always told lies anyway, but it was what all the teachers were trying to make sure that you didn't do. But this was different. She felt that she knew the old woman and old women were safe, like grannies, so long as they weren't witches and witches didn't really exist anyway.

So it was all right.

Anyway the old woman couldn't be a witch, she wasn't smiley and friendly and inviting like a witch would be. She wasn't smiley at all.

Sky was sitting on an old brown seat thing in the caravan. The material was stripy, but it was so old the stripes weren't stripy any more. And it felt sticky and a bit damp. So she wasn't a granny either because grannies had a thing about dampness.

And she didn't ask if it was all right with her mother for Sky to be there which a granny would have done. And she didn't smell like a granny. She smelt sour, the kind of sourness that Sky could imagine you wouldn't smell after a while. Like a cow wouldn't notice its own cow smell, a kind of lived-in smell, dish-clothy and cupboard-under-the-sink smell. It came off her in little puffs as she moved around the space. There was a table, Formica like a granny's kitchen table, and a sink.

And things everywhere, heaps of newspapers and boxes and old plastic lemonade bottles. One of the windows had cardboard over it which was held in place with parcel tape. The old woman shuffled round in a strange kind of automated jerky dance, as if she'd being doing it for ever. She filled a tiny blackened kettle with water from one of the bottles. She glanced, testingly, at Sky. "No tap, see," and then placed it on a little brass thing with wire arm things like coat hangers that held the kettle. It had a bright yellow flame that turned blue.

"Primus," she said, bafflingly, as if it explained everything.

Sky slid her hands beneath her knees and leant forward with what felt like a little hiccup of joy. This was indeed an adventure.

This was how she wanted to live, in a tiny space, with no tap, and seats that you could put dirty shoes on and water from old bottles and a funny stove that only did one thing at a time.

The tea, when it came, ages later was strong and orange and tasted of plastic from the bottles and of carnation milk that had been poured from a tin with two holes punched in the top and brown crusted milk all round it. "No fridge," said the old woman, with a teasing smile that wasn't friendly, and that said if you come here you have to take it as you find it.

So there they sat, Sky on one side of the table and the old woman on the other. And they looked at each other over mugs that were as stained as the old woman's fingers.

"A story?" said the old woman, whose name was Eva. "You want a story?"

Sky nodded, who wouldn't? This would be a story that wouldn't be contained by hard covers and wouldn't end with home-time. It would be free and wild, and crazy as the beach garden.

"A story… You want a story. November… why is it always November? Cold, bitter and the rain stopped. For ever it seemed. Hunger like you can't imagine. Smells, people, shit, urine, babies too weak to do more than whimper. Comfort dimly remembered from a different country. A different lifetime. The ghetto had been bad enough. But survival just. For some. Then there

came talk of work. Factories up in the forests. New camps. Hostels. But I don't think anyone was fooled. Why should they be? Trust would always be the first to go."

Sky listened to the words and it was as if her breathing had stilled. She knew she was at the edge of something big. Because Mrs Patterson had talked to them about it, not at story time but at Assembly. And everyone knew that Assembly stuff and story time stuff were worlds apart and had nothing to do with each other because one was real and the other was story but where the truth was Sky couldn't tell. It had been Holocaust day and Mrs Patterson had put on her serious face, not her sad and disappointed face, that was the one she used for farts and giggles, but the solemn one, and she'd told them about what had happened to the Jews during the Second World War; yellow stars, and cattle trucks, and gas chambers.

And Sky had tried to not remember it.

But that didn't work because it just burrowed more deeply, so she tried to remember it and that was worse because she did.

And here was someone who had done it. Been there. She daren't do anything to break the spell. And she let Mrs Patterson's voice fill in the bits between Eva's words.

"A slit. Ice forming on the outside of the truck. Waiting. And through the slit a slice of countryside, as flat as a dangling bootlace. Black fields. The smell of cabbages. Three people. An old man, an old woman, and a young girl. The November light draining colour from them all. Propped on their hoes. Taking a break to watch the train pass. Only it wasn't passing. All you could hear was the drip of urine onto the track. Freezing into yellow ice."

Numbers, Mrs Patterson had given them numbers, huge numbers of people – killed. And the numbers had been relief because numbers meant you didn't need to think of the singles, the ones; the girl who was ten, a boy who was six.

"Three people. Figures from a fairy tale. Grandfather and grandmother and a fairy princess. Three figures. Then the clanking, creaking in the joints of the trucks. And it slid away. That shred of picture. It jerked and

you almost expected that they'd fall, the three of them at the suddenness of it. It went but not soon enough.

The old man turned to the other two, said something. And looked back at the trucks. He spat and laughed, a black mouth of contempt. And so did they. The old woman and the girl."

And Eva looked up at the filthy window and listened for the distant sound of the careless sea, creeping up among the paths and gardens and walls of the little garden. Almost, Sky thought she could hear the stones tumble from their precarious walls, her own brick tower crash and the feather, upright as a poplar, fall and roll as the sand was sucked away from beneath it.

"The girl. She'd seen the glimpse of flesh through the crack in the side of the truck. The luminous grey-pink of a human face. The eyes of another human being. Peering out at the field. She'd seen it. Human flesh. Human.

And she was the only one who had. The old man and the woman knew. Knew what was in the trucks. They'd seen them day after day. But the girl. She had seen flesh. And I knew she knew. That was it, you see, I knew and I would never forget. That girl, the peasant princess from the fairy tale. I would never forget what she did that November afternoon. Propped on her hoe. And laughing at her grandfather's joke about the flesh and blood cargo on the trucks.

The smell of the field of cabbages. The leaves, cut off and rotting in the frost. Slime like slugs in salt. Cabbage smell like a tramp's fart. Sour. I'd recognise her anywhere. After all those years. I know I would. I see her every day. Every day."

Sky's tea was cold and had an orange scum on the top.

After what seemed like forever Sky said, "What about the gardens? Why do the gardens?"

Eva's hands came flat onto the table to push the old body upright and she turned away.

"Why am I talking to a child about this?" She put her mug in a plastic bowl. Sky could see that once the bowl had been red but the colour had gone from the rim leaving it bleached and waxy pink and the bits lower down had disappeared beneath a layer of grease. It thrilled Sky to know that there were women even worse than her mother at such things.

Eva pulled back her sleeves, first the ancient faded grey green raincoat, and then layer after layer of cardigan and jersey in greys and browns until finally the wrists emerged. Knotted and clad in blue-tinged skin. Sky brought her mug across, amazed that anything should some out of the bowl cleaner than when it went in. It was as batty as the beach garden.

She wanted more from Eva's story; the satisfying cusp of justice that tilted a fairytale into the bed-time comfort and duvet snuggle of good rewarded and bad punished. An ending, and if not an ending a meeting, a chance to say what had to be said. And above all a reason for the garden thing. It had to be something to do with Eva's story of cattle trucks and cabbage fields or she wouldn't have told it. She hadn't after all denied a link

So Sky tried again.

"What happened? Then? After the cabbage field?"

But her mind was suddenly back at school, listening to Mrs Patterson; the rubbery smell of the gym mats and the polish from the floor and watching the vast trunks of Mrs Tindale's legs at the piano as she waited to start the hymn. And Mrs Patterson's words, words Sky had been unable to forget. Something about numbers. Sky watched the arms turning in the filthy water and raising the mug and placing it upside down on an old tin tray with a picture of Windsor Castle on it. Eva's sleeves were up to her elbow. The old woman took an old tea towel, stained and frayed beyond recognition, and dried her hands. The arms twisted and turned as she carefully mopped and pulled at the ancient skin.

Numbers. It had been the numbers that Sky had remembered, because it was numbers that enthralled her and she had hated to think of them being hijacked by such commonplace evil. Eva turned and hung the cloth on a plastic hook on the wall.

And then she began to shake the sleeves back down.

"No," said Sky. "Show me." And she took the old woman's hand and turned it and then the other one. And then she looked into the old woman's eyes. "Where's your number?"

And Eva looked at the little girl.

She didn't say what number, she knew – of course – what Sky was after. And she knew that it was not to be found. No one, in all the times that she had told the story had asked, because everyone had assumed, had known there was only one viewpoint in the story, that no one would ever be able to tell the story from another viewpoint, from the other perspective; the other end of the slit in the cattle truck.

Until this little girl with the silly name came and squatted beside her on the beach.

"You were the girl in the field, weren't you?" said Sky, angry and frightened.

"No," said Eva. She turned her defeated, wobbling head away and her eyes became scratchy with thorns of remorse. "I *am* the girl in the field. I always will be."

"And the gardens?" Sky's voice was tight and strung with terror but she had to know.

"For her. The girl in the truck."

"And it never ends? The making of them?"

"No. It never ends. It can't, you see. Who would I be if I stop?"

And Sky backed away, found the door and ran and ran as fast as she could. She stopped just before the track turned, and she looked back at the figure in the door of the caravan.

The Paper Garden

Sky played a game every time she went home, well, it didn't feel like home but Mum said it would soon, when the stupid people at the bank got their act together, and when the solicitor pulled his finger out and got sorted. And all the other things that Mum complained about when things weren't right. Which was a lot because nothing ever seemed to be right. And the game was this; she had to keep to the edge of the road, well, she had to anyway because there were no pavements in this part of the world, just muddy edges, and long grass and stingy bare hedges that had black branches that you couldn't hide in. And the game meant that with every step you had to tread on at least one blade of grass. It was like not treading on the cracks in the pavement only the other way round. What was the point of being in the country unless there was grass? So you had to tread on it, to make sure you were there. And it knew you were there.

The country was supposed to be a good thing. Mum had said everything would be all right when they got into their new house in the country. But she'd said that about the previous house, and the one before that. So Sky had to do things to make sure that it was going to be all right this time and treading on grass blades was one of them. And this time perhaps the making things all right was going to be a letter from the solicitor or the bank or the building society. Or maybe a letter with handwriting on the front. Which would be the best thing to make it all right. Only that letter never came and anyway Mum would rather have a letter from the solicitor.

Did brown grass blades count? And Sky looked down at her feet to see if it was really dead or only pretending. There was a lot of brown grass at this time of the year. And yellowy stuff and things that she kept wanting to take in to school for the 'Show-and-Tell' table — only that was at the other school, with Mrs Patterson and all her friends. And Sky didn't want to think about it because it made her sad and made Mum go on about a fresh start and being brave and making new friends, and anyway she was always going on about Mrs Patterson at the other school so why did she miss her now? And Sky couldn't think of anything to say to that, just that you knew where you were with Mrs Patterson and it felt safe. Safer even than treading on blades of grass. But that was a secret and she couldn't even begin to tell Mum about that. And now she had another secret because she knew she couldn't tell Mum about the old woman in the caravan near the beach who turned out to be the wrong girl in the story. And she couldn't tell Mum about how she'd started at the new school so late in the term that she didn't have a part in the nativity play. Because Mum might go down to school and make a fuss. Which was much worse even than having a name like Sky. All the more reason to tread on the grass blades. And anyway, it was Saturday and she didn't have to think about the new school and perhaps it was going to be good day, and Mum might be in one of her good moods which was sometimes as scary as the bad ones but at least the food was better. And always odd. They had strange food when mum was feeling better. The kind of food that you would expect a mother who called her daughter Sky would eat; hot spicy food that went with joss sticks and wind chimes, and used lots of pans and bowls and took for ever to cook so that you were really hungry by the time it was ready.

A cottage in the country, that was what Mum had said when she had first told Sky about it, before they had moved in. A cottage near the sea and with a stream running past the kitchen door. Sky tried very hard to make it into a cottage, but mostly she saw a kind of wooden hut thing, like a holiday chalet that had seen better times. And the stream was nowhere.

When she came round the bend in the road she saw her mother in the garden. It wasn't much of a garden, more of a piece of field that had strayed into the wrong place but Sky liked it. They hadn't had a garden before, so she couldn't compare. It had enough hedgey things to hide in and watch the road, which was what she did a lot of. Perhaps the old woman from the caravan would come past and Sky could spy on her and get her own back in some obscure way.

Just the day before Sky had found the stream only it was more like a ditch, and it went under the elder bushes behind the house and when Sky crawled underneath, the smell reminded her of the water butt she could dimly remember from her grandfather's garden. It was her father's father which was why the memory was so faint and distant.

The stream was the best part of the garden and was full of plastic bags and blue scratchy string and purple bricks. And best of all wriggly things that jerked their way over the mud, and when you poked them they wriggled even more and shuffled and shuffled until they came out of the cloudy water and continued on their erratic journeys. She made up stories about them, where they were going and why.

Kirstie, Sky's mum, was standing, her hands on her hips. Her hair, long and just beginning to go grey was lifting slightly in the breeze. The signs were good. She saw Sky and smiled, and waved. It was getting better.

"Darling!" she called. "This is where we're going to put the barbecue. What do you think?" Sky looked at the corner, choked with brambles and nettles that her mother was pointing to. "There's one in the catalogue. Come inside, and I'll show you."

And Sky followed her mother inside. The hall was jammed with boxes. Things that they had brought with them from the other house. There was a mixer that had never been out of its box. And a picnic hamper. And a tent. New starts and beginnings and the answer to all the 'if-onlys' that had spurred her mother on in her daily scouring of the catalogues. The solution to the current problem, to all the snags and hitches, all the people and circumstances who got in the way and stopped her mother being 'herself' and 'fulfilling her potential'. Always the goal was just out of reach, just beyond the particular horizon of the moment.

"Just think," her mother was saying, "next summer, you can have all your new friends round for a barbecue. Won't that be fun? I can just picture it, can't you?"

But Sky couldn't. Not at all. All she wanted was to hide in the hedge and spy on people on the road, or crawl under the elder bushes and watch the creatures wriggling their lives away in the stream. She wasn't good at that thing that her mother did so well, see things in the future. "Just think…" it was the beginning for her mother of so many hopes and for Sky the beginning of a kind of tired failure.

"But you've got to have dreams," Kirstie would say to Sky in exasperation when Sky couldn't go with her on her great sweeping plans that seemed as broad and impossible as the wings of the angel in the window of St

Michael's church in the village. She knew about the church because they had been taken in for a service from school. Sky couldn't remember anything about the service, just the unreachable angel in the window and the smell. And the wonderfully secret secure knowledge that there were a hundred good places to hide in in a church.

The catalogue was out on the kitchen table. Along with the toast crumbs from breakfast and mugs nearly as stained as the old woman's. The room smelt of coffee and the smoke from mum's last cigarette.

"Look, darling. It's only a few pounds a week, and just think of the fun we'll have with it."

Sky looked, and it all seemed a million miles away from her life. There was a picture of people, with orangey brown limbs, in shorts, standing round a black thing on legs. They all had glasses in their hands and grins on their faces. There was a man with an apron on and a large fork thing in his hand. Her tummy wobbled. It would never happen, well, the barbecue would arrive in a box, but there would be no parties and fun, and people with orange legs and drinks, and certainly never a man with an apron. The barbecue would stay in its box and then the letters would arrive, wanting money and mum would curse at them and light a cigarette, and make more coffee. And if it got really bad she wouldn't get out of bed.

And when that happened Sky wanted more badly then ever the letter with proper writing on the outside. Her father's writing, only it never came.

Sky said the things that mum wanted to hear, and pretended that when the barbecue came everything would be all right. That it would be the best thing that they had ever had. The thing that would make everything come right. And perhaps it would. After all Sky hadn't lived as long in the world as her mum. And when mum was in this mood she was so compelling. This time would be the time that it would happen. Sky wanted so desperately to believe that.

After all, things can change. Stories were full of things that change. Stories, Sky decided, were only ever about things that change; frogs into princes, peasant girls into princesses. Only that made Sky think about the old woman in the caravan, and the way her story had turned upside down and made her feel kind of dizzy inside her head, which was worse than feeling dizzy by staying too long on the roundabout in the park by school. Which was what she did after school sometimes so that she wouldn't have to be with the other children.

So she stuck her finger in the sugar bowl and licked it and tried to hold the sugar crystals on her tongue for as long as she could, and went out of the kitchen door to the elder bushes and the stream to watch her friends wriggle.

She put her hand in her pocket and felt the feather that she had picked up from the beach. It was black, and still had the greeny sheen on it from the time when it was still on the bird. But Sky knew it wouldn't last long. It would be as disappointing as conkers, that bright burnish which lasted only from the chestnut tree by the church to the park and had long gone by the time you got it home to show mum. She had thought that it would only be white feathers on the beach, from seagulls, but then she had thought it would be only pebbles on the beach not bricks. Perhaps the black feather came from a crow that had lived in the village under the sea, then Sky realised that was silly, the village must have been ages and ages ago, and the crow was quite recent. She tried to smooth the feather neat again but the frondy bits wouldn't stick together any more. It was impossible to think about it holding a bird up and doing all that air magic. She held it out over the water and let it go.

It sat on the surface for a moment and then turned, with a kind of remembered pattern of previous elegance, and moved, slowly and gracefully down stream. Sky watched it as long as she could, as it slipped into the darker shadow of the bushes, and then was gone. It was the first time that she had thought about the stream, about the fact, and Sky was fond of facts, that it was a stream, and that it was moving. All the time it was moving. However long she stayed there it would never be the same piece of water that went past her, never the same molecules. She liked molecules – it was her second most favourite word – she liked them almost as much as she liked numbers. It felt exciting and frightening all at the same time. Like thinking about stars. Thinking about stars was the only time she ever felt comfy with her name.

And then she thought about pooh-sticks, and her father and things that they did, which didn't take long because he hadn't done much with her only talked about it. But she was sure, well, almost sure, that they had played pooh-sticks. She could see them doing it, so they must have done. That out of all the remembered rememberings must have been a fact. A hazy fact. Where and when were unclear. But thinking about it made her feel good. And the unknown destination of the feather. She suddenly thought that one day her father might be looking over a bridge and see a black feather float under it, and think about pooh-sticks and Sky and remember and wonder. Which was what gave her the idea. A really stupid, daft idea. But the sort of idea that once you've had it you can't get rid of it. She would send him messages down the stream. There was no way, really and truly no way that he would ever get them... but... Things happen. Really crazy things happen. Things turning up when you don't expect them, and animals walking hundreds of miles to get home. People meeting up after years and years and not knowing they were still alive. Really amazing, unbelievable, coincidences.

And so she did.

The first one she just wrote on her best writing paper with the teddy bears all round the edge, and her heart was beating as she crawled under the elder bushes. It took a while for her to let it go. And then, as soon as she had, she realised that it was silly, because the paper would very quickly become waterlogged and sink. And anyway, even if it didn't the writing would go all blurry and no one would be able to read it. So she would have to make a boat for it, a boat that would go backwards or forwards or upside-down. Which was when she had the idea about the plastic bags.

And it became part of another game, watching for the post. She hid in the hedge and waited for the post man. If there was something — junk mail or one of mum's catalogues — that came in a plastic wrapper it meant that she could write another letter. The most exciting and scary bit was cutting the plastic bag off without her mum finding out. Her mum wouldn't have minded her having them but this was something secret and she didn't want her mum to know about it. She didn't know what her mum would think about her writing to her father. Well, she did know, that was the trouble. And mum wouldn't like it.

She put the letter in the bag and puffed air into it and tied it with one of the plastic wire things that she found in the kitchen drawer, and then she practised in the sink. Only she had to empty the sink first which meant that she had to do the washing up. But it worked, the little bubble of a boat bounced on the water and the letter inside looked quite dry.

It was when she was sending the third one that her mother found her. Sky heard the panting and the sound of the twigs being pushed and broken. And felt the thud as her mother lay down beside her in that dark and secret place.

"I said, I said, didn't I say, Sky? That there was a stream?"

And all Sky could think about was the little boat, there on the water in front of them and it didn't seem to want to move, all the others had gone before she had time to think about it, but this one turned and turned and seemed stuck on a little eddy.

"Sky! Just imagine." But Sky couldn't; didn't her mum know after all this time that she couldn't do that? Just imagine? "We'll clear all this stuff away and tidy it up and we'll make it part of the garden. A stream garden. Get rid of all this rubbish and open it up and plant things, bog plants And water lilies. And irises. Yellow and purple irises. I can just see them. Can't you?"

But Sky couldn't. She just felt tentacles of fear reach down into her throat. Prickles as sharp and gaspy as when you suck on a pickled onion and the vinegar goes the wrong way.

"And stones along the edges, and those tall primula things. And you could get some frogspawn, there must be some round here in one of the ditches. I know —your friends at school. You can ask around, maybe one of them has a pond with frogspawn. In the spring. When we've got it all cleared. Got rid of all that rubbish. It's disgusting. Just look at all stuff in there. Ugh... what are those wriggly things?"

Sky couldn't bear to think that her mum was going to spoil it. She wanted the stream as it was with her wriggling friends and the mud and the plastic bottles and purple bricks and blue string and her stupid, futile letters that would never get anywhere further than the field with cows just down the road.

And this one wasn't even getting that far.

"I can't believe how people could just throw all this stuff into a stream," her mum was going on. "It's appalling. How could anyone do it? Look! Look! That's recent. That's only just been thrown in." And before Sky could do or say anything, her mother's long arm had reached across and fished out her letter.

Sky felt as small and wriggly as her friends. She just wanted to be with them and burrow into the mud and stay there forever.

Her mother recognised the teddy bears on the paper. She should, after all, she had given the pad to her. She heard the plastic being torn open. And the silence as her mother read it. And then without a word she heard her mother grunting as she crawled out backwards.

Her mother was waiting for her on the kitchen step. Her hands on her denimed hips. Her face an unreachable pinch of misery.

"He won't come back, Sky. How many times have I got to tell you? He's not coming back. Never. He's had it with us. Can't you understand?"

Her mother stood there, and took up all the space in the kitchen so that Sky was stuck in the garden and couldn't even go into her room.

"How do you know?" Sky's words creaked with despair.

"I know. I know him, it's no good expecting him to come back. It's over. You'll never see him again. Live in the real world, Sky."

And she turned. It was that, the retreating back that did it for Sky.

And she flung herself at her mother. Beating at the brick red jumper. And screaming and screaming. And words coming out that she didn't know she had in her.

"Don't tell me to live in the real world! You never have! You'll never do anything about anything. You'll never use the barbecue or the mixer or clear the stream. Or plant irises. You're useless. You just go on and on about everything stopping you doing things. You can't even do the washing up like a normal mum. It's always about imagining things in the future. How everything's going to be all right tomorrow or next week or next year. It's never about now, about–"

And Sky stopped, scared by what she had said. Things that she hadn't known she'd thought. And then she found she couldn't stop herself saying "You're as bad as the old woman in the caravan. Only she's – she's facing backwards. Neither of you look at what's close at hand."

And she couldn't help saying it because it suddenly seemed so clear and true and awful and she wished more than anything that she could unsay it all and unthink it all. But she couldn't.

And there was, she realised, in it a kind of searing relief, through the fog of bleak horror.

And then because she knew that it was the end of everything, she said, "I hate you." but quietly which was worse than shouted.

And there was her mother's face turned towards her, a grey mask of pain and despair. And her mother was saying, "What old woman?"

"She's a horrible smelly old woman and she lives in a caravan near the beach. And she—" and then Sky realised that she couldn't say what it was that the old woman had done as a child sixty years ago. And the reason she couldn't say it was because taking it back into her head, listening again to Eva's voice meant that she was there in the field with the smell of the cabbages and the truck. And she was in the field, with Eva, not in the truck and she knew with an absolute certainty that she, Sky, was also the girl who had laughed at the Jews in the truck. And knowing that meant that the old woman wasn't horrible, just old and smelly and sad and hung up on the past like the old cloth caught up on a barbed wire fence that Sky passed every day on the way to school and that would just get older and dirtier and more worn out each year.

And looking at her mother's face she knew that she didn't hate her, and that she understood the fear and the invisible black dragon that came after her mother and which snapped at her ankles and drove her to always hook her happiness onto things in the future that would never happen, however

much Sky worked and worked at it to make them happen, by stepping on grass blades and washing up, and trying and trying to see the things that her mother saw in the catalogues.

She could never make her mother happy. And reaching into that knowledge was like getting to the end of a sum at school and knowing that it was true, true like the first time she had climbed over the dunes and seen the sea and the strange lumpy figure that had turned out to be the old woman making her beach gardens.

She could see them, these two women, Eva and her mother, so clearly that it made her heart ache, but she couldn't do anything about them. She turned from her mother's stricken face and left the stream garden and went out into the road and this time instead of heading for the sea she went towards the village and this time she was careful not to tread on the grass blades. That was a babyish thing to do.

Eva and mum would have to look after themselves.

The Well Garden

Sky walked away from the squat ugly little bungalow with a surprising amount of resolve for someone who had just said terrible things to her mother. She walked in the middle of the road. For two reasons; one so that there was no way she would tread on the grass blades at the edge. And the other because she knew it was dangerous, any moment a tractor might come round the corner and run into her with one of those screeching sounds that they always had in 'Casualty', only it was never a surprise since you knew it was going to happen because the cameras followed the character who was going to be hurt and you knew it was only a matter of time.

And then in 'Casualty' there was always a quarrel, well, she'd done that bit, the quarrel.

She worked the idea of being in an accident through her head for a moment. The advantages were this; mum would be sorry and think it was her fault; the horrid girls at school would be sorry and the teacher would make them send a card and some sweets to the hospital; dad might get to hear about it and come and visit her; the old woman in the caravan would think she was to blame because that was what she always did.

But the trouble with accidents like that was that you couldn't stop it at just the right moment, what if she were to die? She thought of her funeral in the church with the angel window, and people weeping and saying nice things about her. They couldn't say the truth because that wasn't what happened at funerals. She'd been to her grandmother's funeral and the man at the front with the frock on had said all sorts of things about grandmother that weren't true. Like that everyone had loved her. Which was obviously not true because she had been a mean person and was responsible for all the things that went wrong in her mum's life. All the things that her dad hadn't caused, anyway. And sometimes her mum said that they were both responsible for everything, which wasn't very logical when you thought about it. And unlikely as her dad and her mum's mother had hated each other, so they weren't going to get together to ruin her life.

The half term holiday was half way over and Sky wished she could hang onto it for ever. She liked the way she could see into gardens more now than when they had first arrived in the summer. She could see into hedges

and places to hide, behind people's sheds and garages. And there were still enough leaves left for the colours to look good, they looked as if they were hiding as well, kind of greys and browns and greasy and slimy, even the yellow ones had lost their glare and had gone blotchy.

Thinking about her funeral had made her brave, so she stomped all the way through the village, and didn't see anyone at all, even though she felt ready for the horridest of the girls at school. Perhaps that was what courage did to you, she thought, made the horrid girls disappear. She even slowed down a little outside the Red Lion in case Mandy, who lived there and smelt of chips and boasted about having coca cola for breakfast, came out. And then Sky could be really brave. But she didn't.

And it was then that Sky had the idea. It was at that point in the village that the stumpy thing could be seen. She'd seen it every day when she walked to school but hadn't thought about it or what it was. And as the trees lost their leaves it had become clearer. She'd be a real spy and find out what it was. It was dark brick colour and stood as tall as the church tower. It looked old and worn, like something that had been rubbed and seeing it behind the trees she thought of the brick tower that she had set up in Eva's garden on the beach.

She turned first left past the pub, down the road past the new houses, which were pretending to be old ones, with little gable windows and steep roofs and patterns in the brickwork until they stopped and the road turned away from the stumpy thing which confused her for a moment but she went on anyway because spies didn't give up.

It was scary because suddenly there were no hedges to hide in and the stumpy thing had gone. On either side of the road there were ditches, with water in them that was black and smelly and didn't move like the stream or the sea. There was a kind of low bridge thing that went over the ditch so that the farmer could go into the field and Sky lay down on it so that she could look into the water.

The water had an oiliness; a dank gluey-ness, and circles of rainbows. She didn't know where they came from. When she stuck her finger in it, the rings danced and shimmered. She felt she could stay for ever in the eternal arcs of colour. But it was cold, and she knew she had to move before the stumpy thing went from her mind.

The road seemed to go on for ever. There were stunted trees, as ugly as the stumps of sprouts in the allotments behind the pub, with knobbly tops and twigs that came out like shock-headed-Peter's hair in the story book at school. The fields behind the ditch were flat and ran away into a distance as level as the sea. Sky wondered what the fields were for, they were empty of anything that looked like animals or grain, or the things that farmers did in stories.

After a few more yards she came to a track that turned off to the right. Logic — which was only like sums with words — told her that this must at least be going in the direction of the tower when she last saw it. Perhaps the tower had disappeared, properly disappeared, like something in a story. Perhaps no one else could see it. Perhaps it would be like the crock of gold at the end of the rainbow. Perhaps she would spend the rest of her life looking for it and never finding it, like Babushka.

The track led back towards the trees, proper trees this time, not the strange ones by the road. Big ones, with lots of water and black sludgy mud between them, the kind of mud that would pull your wellies off.

It was dark under the trees, even though it was only afternoon., and the air was still and cold and silent. Sky felt as though she was the only person in the world.

There was a gate on her right, and a rutted, grassy drive and she knew, absolutely knew, with that kind of knowing that felt like the nearly ending of a good long sum, that it would lead her to the brick tower.

She nearly turned away, left it at that. Left it for something to do on another day, a day when it wasn't so cold and dark and scary. A day when she hadn't quarrelled with her mother. Left it like she sometimes did with a sum, knowing how it would go in the last few exhilarating numbers. Left it like when she and her mum did a jigsaw and they left the last piece and pretended that they couldn't find where it went. Left it because she could always come back to it now that she knew.

But she didn't.

She climbed the gate the way her mum had told her, going over it at the hinge end where it would be stronger and landed with a soft trembling thump on grass that seemed to be hanging on water. The track led away under the trees. And suddenly, with a heart-lurching jolt of fear and joy, there it was, her brick tower, the stumpy thing. And it *was* a stumpy thing *and* a brick tower and everything that she had hoped for. Which was odd because it was only then, when she saw it that she realised how much hope had been involved.

It had a door and windows.

And a man.

And she had arrived so quickly that she hadn't had time to do her spying thing and hide. And there were plenty of things to hide in and behind. It was the best possible place to do that. There were old rusty things, things that looked as if they hadn't moved for centuries, and buildings and sheds and barns and bushes.

And a cat.

She'd wanted a cat, but mum had said no, with that solid sound that meant you couldn't start with something impossible, like an elephant and haggle down to a cat. And it also meant that you couldn't start with something small like a goldfish or a gerbil and work up to a cat.

No cat. Not ever.

Until this one; with its blotchy patterns of white and orange and grey stripy bits. A Heinz cat. It was what her father had said once when they saw a dog that was bits of different ones, and then he had explained it by saying "Fifty seven varieties," which hadn't explained anything. What this cat had which the dog hadn't was a pretty face. And it came up to her and nudged her ankles with its little hard triangle of a head and gave the game away completely.

The man turned from whatever he was doing with a piece of rusty old metal, and stood. He looked across at Sky as if to say "What kept you?"

and his smile was as broad and open as a clown's before things go wrong, before he trips over his outlandish boots or the custard pie flips in his face.

"Fawkes," he said, as baffling as dad's fifty seven varieties. "The cat, he's called Fawkes."

"Why?" said Sky thinking of knives.

"Because my name is Guy. And the cat followed me home one night."

"Oh," said Sky. "I see," but she didn't, not quite. But she went along with it anyway because she liked the man and he thought he'd explained. She bent to stroke the cat who was winding himself round her legs, like a silky rope.

"Have you come to see the pond?"

"I don't know. Have I?"

"I expect so," and he turned and went round the back of the tower. "This way." So Sky followed, knowing absolutely that she had been expected. Which was quite normal for magic towers and people who looked like clowns.

On the far side of the tower was a garden. Not a garden that her mother would have recognised. There was no decking, or paved patio, no barbecue, no bright things in tubs. But then this was a real garden, not a garden on a page in a catalogue. And not a garden that had to be remade every day like the beach garden. It was a real garden and would be there tomorrow and the day after that and the day after that, for ever and ever.

It was a garden that had been worked on and sat in and neglected and left somewhat to its own devices. It would never be finished, there would always be weeds, and a fork stuck in the ground like a bookmark to show where you had got to. There would always be new plans, ideas, 'How about if...', 'Shall I move the buddleia...' but never anything that couldn't be put off until tomorrow or next week.

And always time to gaze into the pond, or watch a grasshopper, or an ant on a blade of grass.

Looking at it made Sky think that the man would understand why she couldn't bear her mother to do anything to her stream. He would understand about her wriggly friends and the secret, hopeless messages to her father. That she had to do it, even though she knew he'd never get them.

There was a brick thing at one side with a wooden cover and over towards the trees was the pond, with tall brown stalks round it. Under a tree with hanging down branches was an old kitchen table, with a cracked Formica top, and two old basket chairs that were green with mould.

Fawkes followed them and peered with Sky into the rich dark surface of the pond. And walked with arrogant grace round the edge of the brick thing that Guy told her was a well. Sky had seen a well in the courtyard of a castle she had been to with her father years ago but she had never thought that you could have one outside your front door.

"Why?" she asked "What's wrong with the tap?"

"There are no taps in the windmill," said Guy and Sky didn't know which piece of preposterous information to take in first. The fact that her brick tower was a windmill or that there were no taps in it. "So," he went on. "I sank the well."

"Oh," she said, because that covered everything. And then, because she had this story-book picture in her head. "Where are the arm things that go round?"

"Oh, it's not a windmill any more. They've long gone."

Sky sat at the table. And Guy brought her out a glass of water.

"Is the well deep?"

"Very."

"Why? I mean why do you need to get water from down there when it's all so soggy round here?" She thought of the ditches by the road and the black lagoons under the trees and his own pond.

Guy laughed.

"Would you like to drink from the pond?"

"Not much, but isn't it all the same water anyway? Just some's on the top and some's below?"

"Yes, but the water in the well is pure. And what's on top is dirty."

"How do you know?"

He took her glass and held it up to the sky.

"I think it'll do. What do you think?"

She took it from him and held it up. She noticed how her fingers through the glass were huge and where the pressure was the skin had gone yellow and fat. And there was nothing nasty in the water that she could see.

"But you can't see germs," Sky said, thinking of Mrs Patterson and a lesson on microbes.

Guy laughed again.

"And how did you know where to do it, the well?"

He looked at her. And his face was suddenly shadowed, the lovely baggy bits falling away from his cheeks without the smile to hold them up. But Sky knew he wasn't sad, just weighing something in his head.

"I'm a dowser." He said. "Do you know what that is?" She shook her head.

"I can find water under the ground, so I knew where to sink the well."

"How?"

Guy looked at Sky for even longer. Then finally he said, "I don't know. Do you think that's odd?"

"What do you mean?"

"Well, I just do it, but I don't know how it works."

"What do you do?"

"I'll show you."

And he went from the table back into the windmill.

Sky thought for a moment about 'stranger danger'. She knew Mrs Patterson would not have been pleased at the way she had sat a the table as if she'd known him for ever or the way she had just let him give her a drink, but then Mrs Patterson would have been equally horrified at the way Sky had climbed over his gate without a 'please' or 'thank you'. All in all she thought it was a good thing that Mrs Patterson didn't know anything about it, and as Mrs Patterson was hundreds of miles away at the other school she was never likely to know. And Sky didn't know if that made her feel safe or scared.

He came back with two bent wire stick things made out of wire coat hangers. Sky was disappointed, she was expecting a trundling machine like the one they had on Time Team. It reminded her of the last time she had seen her dad, driving off in the old car with the aerial made out of a coat hanger.

He laid them on the table with a kind of reverence and pride, as if she would understand and admire.

So she obligingly said, "Wow!" which was, after all, all right because 'wow' was admiration without having to say anything else.

And he showed her how to hold them with the ends out in front of her.

"But," she said, because it seemed so obvious, "How does it work when there's water all around?"

"You have to imagine it, the water, different water fresh and deep in the ground."

And Sky did, she closed her eyes and thought and thought, until she felt dizzy and wobbly, about water that came from so far beneath her feet that it was dark beyond all dark that she could picture. Darker than pulling her duvet over her head in the days when dad was still with them and the shouting started downstairs. Darker than the dark when she crawled under grandfather's shed so that she wouldn't have to go home.

Then Guy told her to walk slowly round the garden. Feeling the grass and the cold and the sounds. She was to stop whenever she wanted to, whenever there was something that was telling her to stop, whenever there was something that she wanted look at or touch or smell, or think about.

At first she felt silly, like a robot with antennae, but there was no one to see her, so that feeling went. And she began to enjoy it, the sense that it was all right just to wander, that wandering with intent was allowed. It wasn't aimless. It had a point; she was looking for water. She could be as nosy and curious as she liked.

She was exploring the bit under the apple trees and trying to avoid the brambles when it happened. It was all the more strange because Guy had not told her what to expect. He'd just told her that she would know when it did. The rods began to move. The ends twitched and Sky felt as if she had something in her hands that was alive. Like when Matthew brought his rat in to school and let her hold it. She stood for a moment and watched the rods. She couldn't stop them moving. The ends began almost to leap and dance until they reached across to each other and crossed. Sky felt shivery and her skin went prickly. She'd almost forgotten about the water under the ground. So far below that she couldn't possibly even hear it trickling.

She couldn't move. It was as if she was paralysed. Held by a force that came up out of the ground and clamped her ankles. Guy was suddenly beside her, huge tender loping strides that brought him across the grass like a gentle stag.

"It's all right," he said and produced an enormous grey hanky for her tears. "It's all right." And he gently took the rods from her.

"It happens," he said. "Sometimes. It happens." And he didn't need to explain what it was that had 'happened'. "With people who are–" But he couldn't finish what he was going to say. And Sky knew without his saying it that it was because of everything that had happened to her, the gaps, the holes in her life, the times when she didn't fit in at school, the times when she wanted to stay on the roundabout in the park and spin and spin until she didn't exist any more, the times when her mum couldn't get out of bed, and the times when the little boat letters went away under the elder bushes in the stream and she knew they'd never make it.

Only it was more than that. It was something bigger. It was all those things that were hers, her story and something more. When she had felt the rods twitch it had opened something inside her, like a kind of tickle, like water running over her hand when she held it in the stream and it made her see things she didn't want to. It made her think about her mum and the quarrel and how her mum was the way she was and would never change but she loved her anyway. And she wanted to cry all over again. And she thought about the old woman and the beach gardens and how Eva would never be free of them.

She even thought about Mandy, at the Red Lion, and what it would be like to smell of chips all the time.

And then dad, with his long grey flecky hair tucked behind his ears and his hefty jerking hands that never knew where to be.

And it all made her feel wild and free and sad at the same time. And large, larger than she had ever felt before. As if she were high up in the sky and could look down on them all.

She looked up at Guy. And wanted to make it all right for him, make it so that he wouldn't feel bad about her crying.

And he smiled at her, "I know" he said. "Let's have a party."

Now, normally parties were things that Sky dreaded, but this was different. She just knew it was going to be all right. It was going to be full of her favourite people, and none of her least favourite people.

And because Guy knew that good things were difficult to wait for he said, "Tomorrow." And they drew up a guest list of two.

Which is how Sky and her mum and Eva found themselves walking towards the windmill-that-wasn't the next afternoon.

And it was all as she remembered and more so. She so wanted mum and Eva to like it that she found she could hardly breathe with the tightness in her chest. Guy took them into the mill and it was as magical as a fairy tale. The room had a curved wall. And brick floors. And it smelt of flour, at least

Sky so much wanted it to that it did. At least it was musty and there were bits of straw on the floor. And some of the old machinery was still there.

It was going to be a party like she'd never been to before. There would be no jelly and ice cream, and none of those awful games which she was always so bad at.

Instead she found that they had to do it all themselves.

Guy gave her mum a fork and showed her where the potatoes were. Eva got given a knife, and told to bring in a cabbage. Guy looked Sky and smiled, "Come with me," he said and they went out to the garden. He lifted her onto the table beneath the apple tree. And pointed to an apple in the branches.

"There," he said. "It's the last one. They are always the best. All the sap and juice, all the energy from the tree is concentrated in that apple. It's its last fling, its last desperate attempt to live. It's like the youngest child. You'd not believe the love that went into it. The tree's hung onto it even while it's losing its leaves. It's yours. Been waiting for you." And Sky remembered that feeling when she first came into Guy's garden of being expected, waited for. She glanced down at him. He smiled and nodded. She reached up and felt the apple in her hand. It hung in her hand smooth and cool and waxy. She bounced it and the branch danced over her head.

"Give it the smallest twist," said Guy.

She did and she heard the tree sigh and click as the apple dropped into her hand.

They sat around the table in the mill as they waited for the potatoes and the cabbage and the fish to cook. Guy brought a jug of water and glasses. And Sky told them about the well and dowsing for water and how it felt. And they all held up their glasses and looked at the water and nodded in admiration, at least Sky hoped it was admiration. Eva, who had not said a word, suddenly started to talk and she told a story only it wasn't the story in the cabbage field, it was another one about her childhood in Poland. A funny one, that made them all laugh.

Sky hadn't believed that Eva was capable of making anyone laugh. And when she caught Eva's eye she realised that Eva hadn't either. And then her mum told them about a disastrous holiday they had had when her dad was still around and that made everyone laugh too. And sky realised that it was the first time her mum had spoken to anyone else about dad. Which meant that it wasn't a secret any more.

The meal when it came was strange because Sky knew that mum didn't like fish but she actually went and had seconds, and Sky definitely didn't like cabbage. But it tasted all right, better than all right. And Eva just kept her head down and ate everything on her plate as if she'd never eaten before in her life. And Guy went about it as if it were special, not just any old meal like you could have on any day. Like as if this was the first meal and the last meal, the only meal. Which was silly, but she knew that he was right, because you never knew.

Sky thought about walking home with mum and giggling with her about a party that had cabbage in it. And how she could never tell anyone at school about it.

And when they had all finished that part Guy nodded to Sky and she fetched the apple and a knife and told them all about it and picking it from the tree.

She put it on a plate, a plate with blue flowers on, and took the knife and cut it into two and then two again. It was only an apple and not very big at that, but when you had told its story it seemed enough to have a quarter each. And Guy had been right, it tasted of all the apples the tree had ever borne.

At the end of the meal Eva put her hand in her pocket and then reached her closed fist across to Sky.

"Here," she said, opening her fingers. And there on the bare boards of the table was the little brick tower.

Lightning Source UK Ltd.
Milton Keynes UK
UKHW052239150222
398731UK00002B/89